ANIMAL
HEROES

D0525123

Stories by Judy Waite and Celia Warren

Illustrated by Derek Brazell,
Kaye Hodges and Kathryn Prewett

Contents

Icy Danger

Playing in the snow is fun, but snow can also be very dangerous.
Shona and Mark found this out one cold day in January.

It had snowed hard all night and it was still snowing.
"You'll never get to school in this weather," said Mum. "You had better stay at home today."

"Great!" said Mark.

"We can play in the snow!" said Shona.

"I must go out to the shop," said Mum.
"Will you be all right on your own?"

"Poppy will look after us," said Mark.

"Woof!" said Poppy.

"OK," said Mum, "don't do anything
silly. I'll be back as soon as I can."

Mark and Shona went out into
the garden.

"Let's make a snowman," said Shona.

"I've got a better idea," said Mark.

"Let's make an igloo."

"Great!" said Shona. "Poppy can
help us."

But Poppy wasn't much help.

She kept jumping on the bricks of snow.

"Get lost, Poppy!" shouted Mark.

"You're no help at all."

Poppy looked sadly at Shona.

"Sorry, Poppy," she said, "I think
you'd better go inside and stay in
your basket."

So Shona took Poppy inside.

Mark and Shona got on
quickly without Poppy.
Mark made the snow bricks and
Shona built the igloo.
Then Mark cut a hole in the side to
make a door and Shona made a
tunnel to the door. At last there was
just one gap in the roof.

Mark slid along the tunnel into the
igloo. Shona pushed a snow brick in
after him.

"Put this in the roof," she said.

"Then our igloo is finished."

"It's going to make it very dark in
here," said Mark.

"I'll get my torch from the house,"
said Shona.

Poppy wagged her tail when Shona came into the house.

"OK, Poppy," she said, "you can come out again."

Poppy stuck her head inside the igloo tunnel and gave a loud bark as if to say, "I don't like it in here."

Shona slid inside the igloo with the torch. Inside, the walls glowed in the torchlight.

"Put the last brick in place," said Shona.

Mark fitted the snow brick into the gap.

"This is great!" said Shona.

Outside it was still snowing.
The trees in the garden were
heavy with snow.
A branch on one of the trees was
bending very low over the igloo.
Then suddenly ...
SNAP!
CRASH!
The branch broke off.
It fell right on top of
the igloo.

The igloo was crushed under a pile of
snow. Mark and Shona were trapped.
Shona called out to Mark.
But Mark did not answer.
Shona was frightened.
It was very dark and very cold under
the snow. She couldn't move to find
the torch and she didn't know if
Mark was OK.

Shona called to Mark again but
there was still no answer.
A lot of snow lay on top of him and
he was not moving.
Shona felt very frightened.
Was Mark hurt? Could he be dead?

Suddenly, Shona heard something.
It was Poppy! Poppy was
digging them out!
"Mark!" shouted Shona. "Poppy is
digging us out!"
"I'm cold!" said Mark.
"Mark! You're alive!" she said.
"Don't worry, Poppy will save us."

But then Poppy stopped digging.

"No, Poppy!" shouted Shona.

"Keep on digging. You've got to get
us out!"

But Poppy had gone.

"I hope Mum will be home soon,"
said Shona.

"Mmm," said Mark weakly.

But what if Mum is delayed in
the snow? thought Shona.

Just then they heard a shout.
And Poppy gave a loud bark as if
to say, "Over here!"
"Mark! Shona!" shouted Mum.
"It's OK. Poppy and I will get you out."
Mum and Poppy began to dig as
fast as they could.

At last Mum pulled Shona and Mark out of the snow.

They were very cold and very wet, but not badly hurt.

"Poppy tried to dig you out on her own," said Mum. "Then she came to get me. She saved your lives."

"Thanks, Poppy. You were a great help after all!" said Mark.

The Terrible Accident

Many children like going to the zoo.
It's a safe way to see wild animals.
But accidents *can* happen.

Joe and Lucy went to the zoo with
their mum and dad. Lucy is Joe's little
sister. She's only two so Joe has to help
look after her.

Joe wanted to see the elephants first.
The elephants were having a bath.
Lucy ran too near the hose and got
very wet! Joe laughed but Lucy
began to cry.
"Don't laugh at her," said Dad.
"Be nice to your sister."

Next Mum bought them all an
ice cream. Lucy dropped her
ice cream on the ground.
Joe laughed but Lucy began to cry.
"Don't laugh at her," said Mum.
"You should look after your sister."

Then Lucy wanted to see the gorillas.

There were two female gorillas.

One had a baby gorilla in her arms.

There was a big male gorilla too.

His name was Buster.

He was sleeping under a tree.

Everyone wanted to get a good
look at the gorillas.
They were all pushing to the front.
"Help your sister," said Dad.
"She's only little."
So Joe took hold of Lucy's hand and
pushed his way to the front.
But the gorillas were down in a pit.
Lucy couldn't see them.

"I can't see the gorillas!" cried Lucy.
So Joe helped her to stand on the
wall and Lucy held on to the bars.
Joe turned round to look for Mum and
Dad. They would be pleased that
he was helping Lucy.

But, just then, Lucy climbed over the bars.

"Joe!" shouted Dad. "Grab her!"

But it was too late.

Lucy slipped right down into the gorilla pit. Everyone started screaming and shouting.

Joe pushed his way through the shouting people. All he could think of was getting to Lucy. A zookeeper was running into the gorilla pit. Joe ran in after him.

Then, suddenly, the zookeeper
stopped running. He stood very still.
"Oh no!" he said.

Joe stood still too. He looked at the
gorillas. One of the females was
holding the baby gorilla.

The other female gorilla was
holding Lucy!

The crowd went very quiet.
Everyone stood still.
Lucy was very still too.
She did not cry but she was very
frightened. Slowly the zookeeper
crept closer to the female gorilla.
Joe kept close behind the zookeeper.
Buster, the big male, was still
asleep under the tree.

But then Buster woke up!
When he saw the zookeeper in the
pit he beat his chest and bared his
teeth. Then the zookeeper saw Joe.
"What are you doing in here?"
he shouted. "Get out! It's dangerous!"
Just then Joe and the zookeeper
watched in horror as Buster went
over to the female gorilla and
grabbed Lucy!
"Joe!" screamed Lucy.

Joe was very frightened.

He didn't know what to do.

The zookeeper tried to get near Buster
but Buster bared his teeth again.

"Joe!" cried Lucy, as she held out
her arms.

Then Joe walked slowly up to Buster
and held out his arms too.

Buster and Joe looked at each other.
Lucy stopped crying but she still
held out her arms to Joe.
Joe held out his arms too.
He kept looking into Buster's face.
Then slowly Buster handed Lucy
over to Joe!

Joe held Lucy tightly in his arms.
Buster looked at Joe and Lucy.
Then he turned to the other gorillas
and gave one of them a playful hug.
Then he jumped onto his swing as if
nothing had happened.

Quickly, the zookeeper hurried
Joe and Lucy out of the gorilla pit.
Mum and Dad were waiting outside.
They gave Lucy and Joe a big hug.
"Well done, Joe," said Dad.
"You and Buster saved Lucy's life."

Trapped!

Jon was looking forward to
going fishing with his grandad.
But it turned out to be a day he
would never forget.

Jon and Grandad set up their
fishing rods in the dockyard.
There was a boat tied up nearby.
"I used to work on a boat like that,"
said Grandad. "My boat was called
'DEEP SOUTH'."

Jon and Grandad sat for a long
time, but they didn't catch any fish.
Then Jon saw a cat.
"Look at that cat," he said.
"It's very thin."
"She's a stray," said Grandad.
"She hasn't got a home."
"I expect she wants some fish,"
said Jon.

Jon looked at the stray cat.
"I haven't got any fish for you," he
said. "Do you like cheese sandwiches?"
Jon threw the cat a sandwich.
The cat crept towards it.
She grabbed the sandwich and ate it.
Then she ran away.

Jon and Grandad still hadn't
caught any fish.

"I'm fed up," said Jon. "I think I'll
go and explore."

"Be careful, Jon," said Grandad.
"Don't go too far."

"I won't," said Jon.

The dockyard was exciting.
There were lots of things to look at.
Jon saw an old warehouse.
He looked in through the broken door.
He could see lots of old planks of
wood inside. On one plank he could
see some writing. He thought he could
read the words 'DEEP SOUTH'.
That was the name of Grandad's boat!

Jon was very excited. He wanted to
get the plank of wood for Grandad.
He ran into the warehouse.
But he tripped on the planks of wood
and fell over. Some of the planks fell
on top of him. His leg was trapped.

"Help!" he shouted.

But nobody could hear him.

Jon was scared. He could see
out through the broken door.

He could see Grandad looking for him.

"Help!" shouted Jon. "I'm trapped!
Over here!"

But Grandad couldn't hear him.

Suddenly, Jon heard a noise.
Something brushed against his back.
Urgh! he thought. It's a rat!
Jon tried to get away but he couldn't
move his leg. Jon was very scared.
What if the rat bit him?

Then something brushed against Jon's neck. Jon closed his eyes.

The rat was going to go for his throat.

But then Jon heard a 'meow'.

It wasn't a rat. It was the stray cat!

"I'm glad you're here," said Jon.

"I don't feel so scared now."

The cat stayed with Jon.

Then Jon heard a loud noise.
There was a bulldozer outside.
It was coming straight for the
warehouse!
"Oh, no!" cried Jon. "It's going to
knock down the warehouse!"
The bulldozer got closer and closer.
The noise got louder and louder.
The cat jumped up and ran away.
"Help!" cried Jon. "Help!"

Suddenly, Jon heard a workman
shouting, "Go away you stupid cat!"
The cat was sitting in the doorway!
The workman kept shouting, but the
cat would not move.
"Help! Help!" cried Jon, as loudly as
he could.
But no one heard him. The bulldozer
was making too much noise.

The workman tried to chase the cat
away. But still the cat would
not move. Then the workman looked
into the warehouse and saw Jon.
"Stop the bulldozer!" he shouted to
the driver.

Grandad hurried over.
He saw the workman helping
Jon out of the building.
"What were you doing in there?"
asked Grandad.
"I thought I saw the words
'DEEP SOUTH' on a plank of wood,"
said Jon. "I thought it was from your
old boat."

The workman went into the
warehouse and came out with a
broken plank of wood.

"This should have been on the door,"
he said. "It says 'KEEP OUT'."

"I thought it said 'DEEP SOUTH'!"
said Jon.

"You are silly," said Grandad.
"But you're safe now."

"It was the cat that saved me," said
Jon. "She made the bulldozer stop."

The next week, Jon went fishing with his Grandad again. But this time Jon brought a big fish with him!
He gave the fish to the cat.